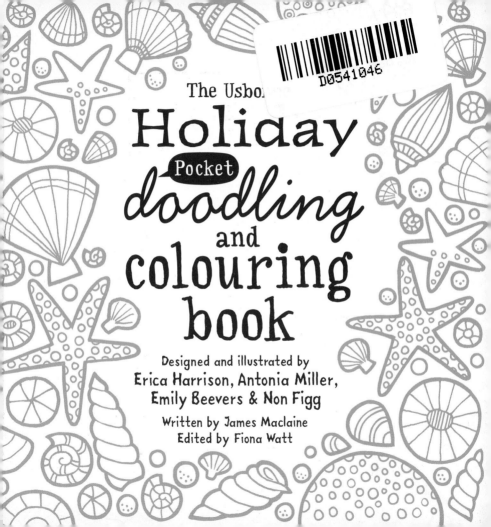

# The Usborne Holiday
## Pocket
# doodling
## and
# colouring
# book

Designed and illustrated by
**Erica Harrison, Antonia Miller,
Emily Beevers & Non Figg**

Written by James Maclaine
Edited by Fiona Watt

2

Doodle more waves and fish, then colour them in.

3

Add lots of spots, patterns and stripes.

4

5

Finish the trees. Draw more birds and fish, too.

6

Use pens to fill the pages with holiday doodles.

12

Turn the shapes into beach huts.

13

Add more track to the roller coasters...

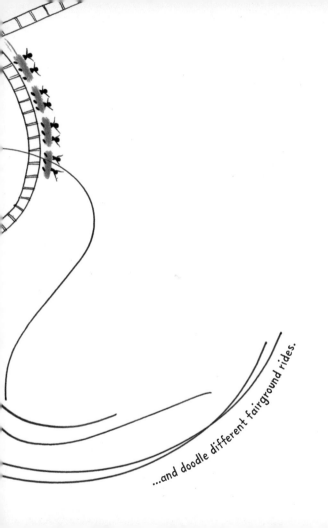

...and doodle different fairground rides.

Draw people on sledges whizzing down the slopes.

Doodle more pine trees, too.

19

Draw more sailing boats on the sea and seagulls on the rocks.

Doodle rippling waves, too.

23

Colour in the fireworks. Draw more windows on the houses and tiles on the roofs.

25

Doodle colourful butterflies across the pages...

...and some flowers, too.

Turn these fingerprints into sea creatures.

Add legs or tentacles...

28

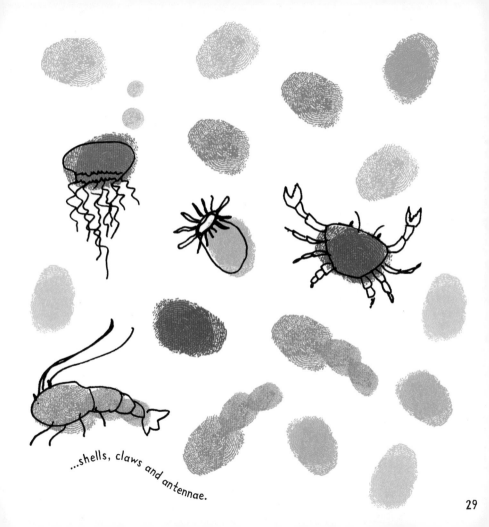

...shells, claws and antennae.

29

Using the squares as a guide,
draw more sandcastles.

Decorate them with flags and shells.

Fill the pages with more bright, pretty patterns.

34

35

Draw a pair of glasses on each face.

Draw more faces and doodle on them, too.

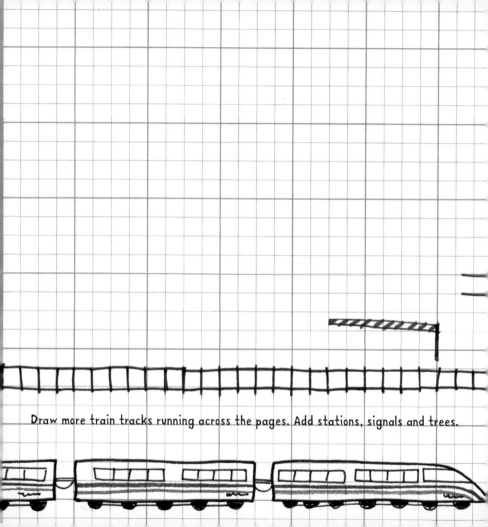

Draw more train tracks running across the pages. Add stations, signals and trees.

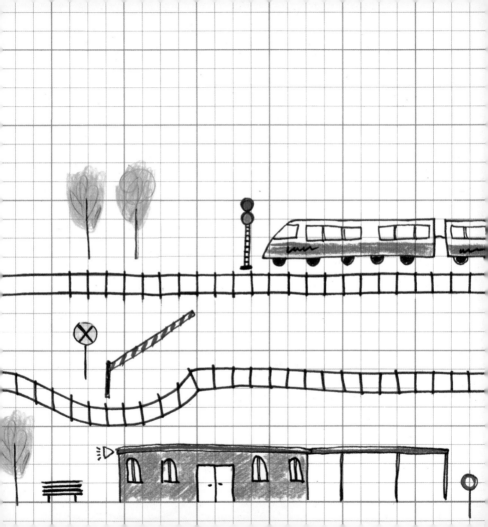

Decorate the beach bags with different designs.

42

Colour in the camper vans.

Turn these shapes into different sea creatures.

44

45

Doodle more tents and caravans at the campsite.

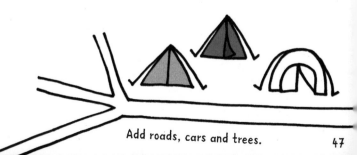

Add roads, cars and trees.

FH213

48

Turn the shapes
into buildings in a
seaside town.

Add more boats tied up in the marina.

49

Divide each kite into four sections...

...then draw different patterns.

53

Finish the canal boats and add more signs.

20

Scribble on the clouds and doodle birds in the sky.

55

Doodle more colourful beach shoes.

57

Draw more tropical fish hiding in the weed.

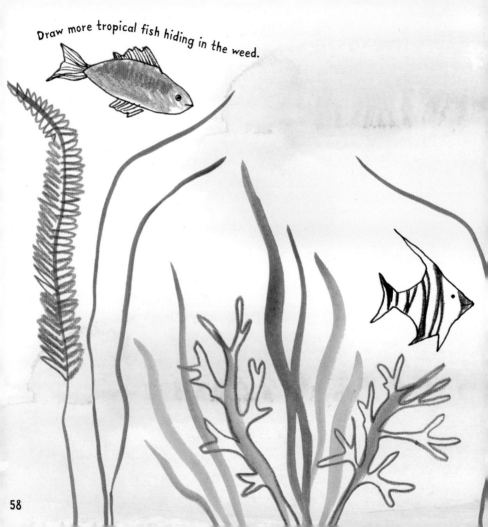

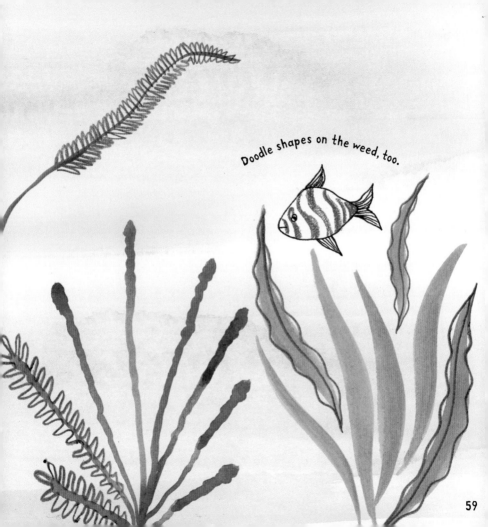

Doodle shapes on the weed, too.

Doodle more ancient ruins...

...trying not to lift your pen off the paper.

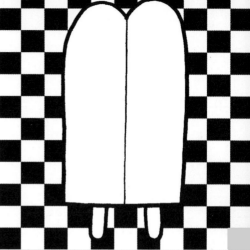

Colour in the ice creams,
lollies and sundaes.

Doodle more performing dolphins...

...and add people to the crowd.

Decorate the surfboards.

66

Give the owls glasses.

Then, fill in their feathers.

Give the suitcases different expressions.
Some could be happy, others could be sad?

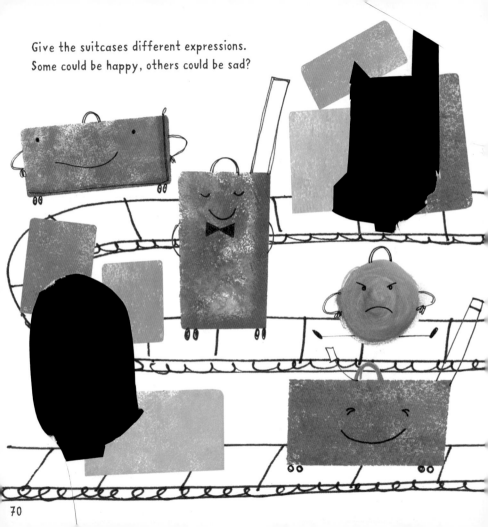

71

Follow the lines to draw more boats and waves.

Doodle more people playing in the sea.

Doodle a different pattern in each of the sun's rays.

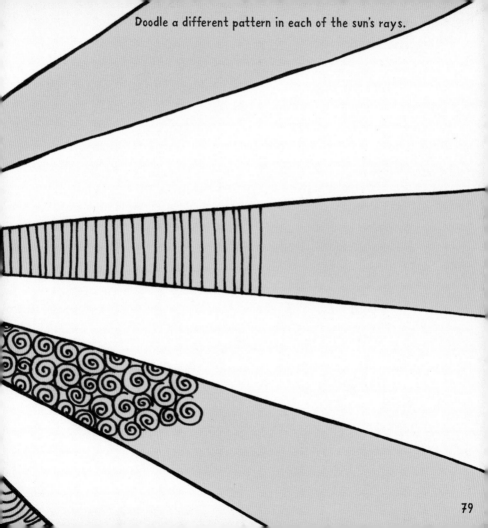

Draw more things you might
pack to take on holiday.

82

83

Add more surfers on the waves.

Use a black pen to complete this tropical sunset scene.

Doodle more patterns on the bunting.

Draw lots more trees...

...and ski chalets in the snowy mountains.

 Draw more cars, bikes and people stuck in a traffic jam.

98

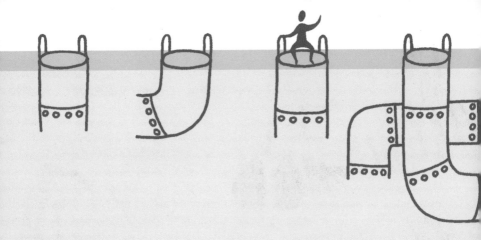

Fill the pages with winding water slides.

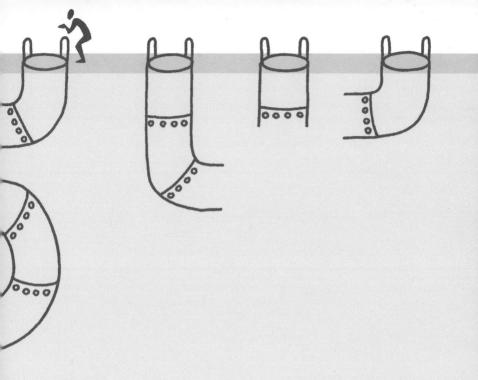

Colour in the buses and draw more passengers in the windows.

Add more patterns to the jellyfish.

Turn these shapes into faces. Give them hats, glasses and sunglasses, too.

Doodle patterns on the seagulls.

Doodle more faces on the ice creams.

110

Give them arms
and legs, too.

Use pens and pencils to finish the planes.

112

113

Colour in the elephant...

...then decorate this one, too.

Draw more colourful hot-air balloons.

Keep doodling skyscrapers without taking your pen off the paper.

Draw more boats in the harbour.

Colour...colour...

Doodle more people on their bicycles.

127

First published in 2011 by Usborne Publishing Ltd., Usborne House, 83-85 Saffron Hill, London EC1N 8RT, England.
www.usborne.com © 2011 Usborne Publishing Ltd. All rights reserved. No part of this publication may be
reproduced, stored in a retrieval system or transmitted in any form or by any means, electronic,
mechanical, photocopying, recording or otherwise without the prior permission of the publisher.
The name Usborne and the devices ♀ ⊕ are Trade Marks of Usborne Publishing Ltd.